DOCKSIDE EXTRAS

STAGE
6
BOOK 1

WHAT COULD
BE WORSE?

John Townsend

CHAPTER 1

"What's your worst nightmare in the whole world?" JJ asked. He'd felt ill all day and was going to bed early.

Rich replied, "It would be waking up with your snake in my bed — about to swallow me whole!"

"It would be worse to wake up with your smelly unwashed T-shirt on my pillow. Ugh!" Tasha laughed.

"Why do you ask, JJ?" Dad said.

"I've had scary dreams all week and I always wake up freaked-out. What ghouls and ghosts will I dream about tonight?" JJ replied.

"Sleep well, love," Mum called. "I hope you feel better in the morning. If not, don't go to school. I'll see what I can get from the chemist to help you sleep and for your stomach ache."

Much later, when Rich was getting into bed, he saw a shadow moving outside his window.
"Who's out there?" he whispered.

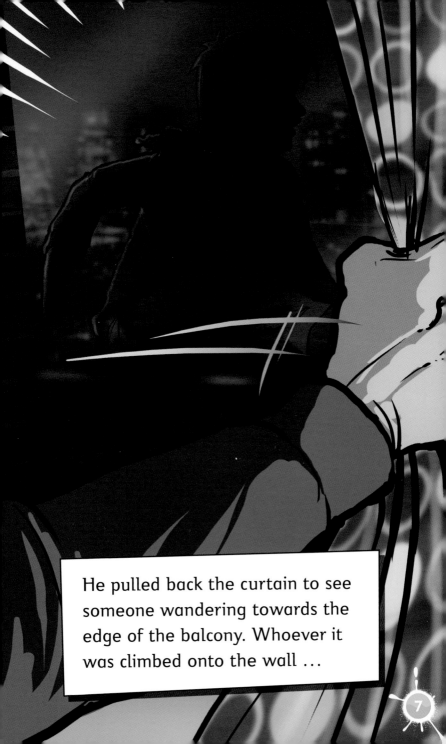

He pulled back the curtain to see someone wandering towards the edge of the balcony. Whoever it was climbed onto the wall ...

Rich ran onto the balcony. "Who are you? What do you want?" he shouted. It was then he saw it was JJ. Rich grabbed him just in time and pulled him back. "Whatever are you doing, JJ?"

JJ looked up at him in a daze. He tried to talk but no words came — just a whimper. "Are you OK?" Rich asked.

"I'm not sure," JJ whined feebly.

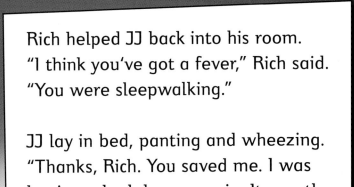

Rich helped JJ back into his room.
"I think you've got a fever," Rich said.
"You were sleepwalking."

JJ lay in bed, panting and wheezing.
"Thanks, Rich. You saved me. I was
having a bad dream again. It was the
worst nightmare ever."

CHAPTER 2

The next day Rich went into JJ's room. "I'm checking you're OK. No more sleepwalking today!"

"That was the worst night ever," said JJ, still looking dazed.

"You'll be fine," Rich said. "I've read up a bit about sleepwalking. It happens a lot. It says boys sleepwalk more than girls, but look at this true story. You asked what would be the worst nightmare in the whole world ..."

news

A sleepwalking girl climbed right to the top of a crane.

She walked from her bedroom to a building site while she was asleep.

She went up the crane and along a narrow beam 40 metres high, where she lay down fast asleep. Firefighters had to rescue her.

"You really know how to cheer me up," JJ said.

CHAPTER 3

When Rich walked to work by the docks, he saw a crane and remembered the true story. "I hope that's not JJ asleep up there!" he thought.

He looked up and suddenly froze when he saw a boy lying across the beam high above him.

Rich ran to a mechanic working on a truck with chrome wheels, shiny exhaust and a huge winch on the back. "Can we use this vehicle to get that sleeping boy down?" he called.

The mechanic made a loud whistle that echoed around the docks. The boy moved and waved weakly. "He's awake," said the mechanic. "Climb on board and I'll lift you up to him."

Rich rose high above the docks where he lifted the boy to safety. "Did you sleepwalk up there?" he asked.

"It was a dare," the boy whimpered. "I got stuck and my friends ran off. I froze with fright. It was the worst hour of my life."

JJ looked much better when Rich got home.

"I'm so glad you're OK, JJ," Rich said caringly. "For a moment today I thought someone was you. To be honest, it was my worst nightmare in the whole world."

1. Why was JJ going to bed early?

2. What was Tasha's worst nightmare?

3. What did Rich see on the balcony?

4. Why was JJ sleepwalking?

5. What true story did Rich find?

6. How did the boy get stuck up the crane?

7. What turned out to be Rich's worst nightmare?

FIND

*Find the **verbs** to fill the gaps.*

1. He saw a shadow _____ outside his window. (page 6)

2. "Whatever are you _____, JJ?" (page 8)

3. Rich ran to a mechanic _____ on a truck. (page 17)

What's missing?

1. why do you ask jj dad said   (page 4)

2. whos out there he whispered   (page 6)

3. are you ok rich asked   (page 8)

*Find the **adverbs** to fill the gaps.*

1. "I'm not sure," JJ whined _____.   (page 8)

2. He looked up and _____froze.   (page 16)

3. The boy waved _____.   (page 17)

4. "I'm so glad you're OK, JJ," Rich said _____.
(page 20)

Which word in the story means

1. puffing or gasping?   (page 11)

2. save or set free?   (page 14)

3. gleaming?   (page 17)

4. a challenge?   (page 18)

*Swap the word in **bold** for a new word that means the opposite.*

5. He saw a shadow moving **outside** his window.

6. That was the **worst** night ever.

7. She walked to a building site while she was **asleep**.

8. He lifted the boy to **safety**.